A
Most
Wondrous
Place

This book belongs to:

A Modestly Illustrated Story by

John Spiers

John Spiers

ISBN 978-1-7366338-0-9

April 2021

GraciePress.com

Dedication

For Gracie and Bessie,
"The Two Best Friends Ever"

Contents

Preface

Life seldom goes quite the way we expect or plan. For many years, I imagined being a great artist and a writer of inspiring books about art. My home would have a huge studio and a library filled to the ceiling with books. People would visit to hear what I had to say and to enjoy the wonderful place I had made.

But those things didn't happen. I live in a small house in a big city surrounded by even bigger cities. I also have chickens in my backyard.

If you were to visit us, you would see my studio is just a corner of the sunroom where I raised my first baby chicks. You would find stacks of books in every room. And you would likely not come to hear what I have to say at all. Instead, you would come to hear what my chickens have to say. And if you were to ask any of them, they would tell you, "This is A Most Wondrous Place."

It is not possible to draw A Most Wondrous Place. But it is possible to write about it, and that is exactly what I have done in this modestly illustrated book.

My life with Gracie has taught me sometimes the things we want in life don't ever happen, but if we look, there will be something much better for us. And when we are searching for that something much better, it often helps to look in A Most Wondrous Place.

Thank you for reading.

John Spiers

Prologue (A Conversation With Gracie)

"What are you doing?" asked Gracie.

"I'm making some pencil sketches of you and the others so I won't forget any of you."

"You aren't forgetful. You always remember to feed us."

"Sometimes people forget even though they don't want to forget, especially when they get old. So I want some words and some pictures to help me remember."

"What will you do with all these words and pictures?"

"I think I will put them in a book and maybe share the book with other people."

Gracie thought this over carefully. "Do they need to remember us too?"

"They need to know how special you are and how much wisdom you have."

"I don't know if I have any wisdom."

"Well, you do. You have taught me more about life than I can ever write or draw."

"Are you sure? You're so much bigger than me. You've got to know a lot more than me."

"There are a lot of big people who need your kind of wisdom. You know heart things, Gracie. That's what matters. You also know about what makes somewhere A Most Wondrous Place."

"Don't people know about that?"

"I didn't know until you helped me learn about it."

Gracie smiled her most delighted smile. "People like secrets and surprises, don't they?"

"You know they do, just like you chickens do."

"Are you going to tell about Bessie and how she likes to bake?"

"Maybe in another book."

"Are you going to tell about Pearl and how she puts on comedy shows for all of us in the backyard?"

"Maybe in another book."

"Are you going to tell about Amelia and how she wants to be the first chicken to fly to the moon and back?"

"Maybe in another book."

I could guess her next question because she was too hesitant to ask it.

"And as much as I want to tell about how you dance ballet, I will do that in another book too. It will be the most special book of all."

"But you promise you will?"

"I promise, and we can work on it together."

There was still something troubling her.

"What else do you want to know, Gracie?"

"In the ballet book, can you draw a picture of me dancing with you in the streets of Paris? I don't think we will ever really get to dance there together." There was a touch of sadness in her voice.

Chickens can do a great many marvelous things like dancing ballet, but traveling to Paris is probably not one of them.

"Of course, Gracie. Drawing lets you do things you would never be able to do any other way."

"Why are you drawing all of the pictures of us when we were very young? Even before we got our combs and wattles?"

"Because I don't ever want to forget when you were My Little Gracie and how I could see the world all over again for the first time through your eyes."

"So what will this book be about?"

"It will be about how our little flock became a family and what you chickens really mean when you say somewhere is A Most Wondrous Place."

"I like that very much," she said.

"I thought you would."

SPRING

March Daffodils

Sometimes the most wonderful things happen by chance. Selecting baby chicks can be that way. Finding a forever friendship can be that way too. At least, that is how it was with Gracie and me.

My life with Gracie began when I was unemployed. Suddenly there was enough time to raise baby chicks. They would keep me busy and looking towards the future. It is difficult to feel sorry for yourself when you are holding a little ball of fluff that looks up into your eyes so innocently and then says, "Peep!"

That spring day, I made two trips to The Feed And Seed Store. On the first trip, I hand-selected the baby chicks to take home with me. Few things are any cuter, and so I went back for more. Those were just scooped up randomly by the sales clerk. Without the second trip back, there would be no Gracie and Bessie in my life. Without that second trip, you would not be reading this.

Including Gracie and Bessie, there were fourteen chicks to raise in my sunroom. Eight were for friends. Six were for me. Those were some of the busiest and noisiest but altogether happiest days of my life.

There were several different kinds of baby chicks in my brooder box. Somehow each kind knew, "You're like me!" But even among the other Buff Orpington chicks, there was always a special bond between Gracie and Bessie. With best friends, you simply know.

Gracie looked a little different. With the others, the feathers above their beaks were even. Gracie's were not, and so her face seemed slightly lopsided.

The first week, a small lump appeared on Gracie's side near her thigh. As the weeks went by, it grew with her. Sometimes it kept her from moving like the others. Even so, she did her best to act like them. She didn't want to get picked on by the more active and assertive chicks.

She stayed close to Bessie whenever she could. Bessie would go off to play with the others, but she always came back to Gracie. They slept beside each other, perhaps more by Gracie's choice, but Bessie didn't mind. It's just like that with friends.

Most mornings after the spring showers, I would collect earthworms from under the bricks and logs outside. While the others were enjoying these treats, Gracie stayed back from the excitement. When it was over, she would go to Bessie. Sometimes she was lucky and found a small earthworm the others had overlooked.

Once I picked her up out of the brooder box and tried hand-feeding an earthworm to her. She was missing out on so much, but she wouldn't eat. Being with Bessie was more important than even a tasty snack.

Gracie was slow to develop, and I wasn't sure she would ever lay any eggs. Bessie started laying almost two months before her. Gracie worried about this.

During the long waiting period, I would tell Gracie every day, "It's okay. You don't have to lay eggs for me to love you. Even though that is what hens usually do, if you can't, I will still love you. I will never get rid of you. It's a promise. You will always be my best girl ever, just like Bessie."

Over time, Gracie began talking to me too. First only a few words, then more as her trust grew. Eventually, we would have long heart-to-heart conversations, but whether in English or Chicken, I really can't say. Languages blend together in the heart. That is where real and true listening begins even when everyone is perfectly quiet.

One of the first things Gracie told me about was her time at The Feed And Seed Store. It had been a scary place for her.

"I stayed close to Bessie in the big box with the heating lamp. There would be a shadow blocking the light. Then a hand would scoop some of us up. I didn't know what happened to those taken away. But I hoped it would be for the better when it happened to me. More than that, I hoped it would be with Bessie."

"So do you think it was all by chance that the two of you ended up here?" I asked. "You weren't in the first group that I brought home. It was only because those others were so cute that I went back and got you and Bessie. Even then, it was the sales clerk who picked you out and not me."

"Maybe some of it was chance," she said. "But you didn't tell the sales clerk to put me back. Even when you noticed my face was not perfect like Bessie's, you didn't tell the sales clerk to put me back. I trust a good heart more than chance. Your eyes told me we mattered and you would be taking us to A Most Wondrous Place."

"Well, this little garden here in the city is nice, but I'm not sure it's all that wonderful. It does need some work."

"It may not be wonderful to you, but it is most wondrous to us. That is what I called it because that is what it is. Not every wonderful place is wondrous. But every A Most Wondrous Place is wonderful."

This seemed like a riddle and a very fun riddle too. She smiled at how her words gave my face a curiously delighted expression.

"What does A Most Wondrous Place mean, Gracie? To a chicken."

"It is not something that can be described. It is not something you can easily point to and say, 'Oh, look at that! It is A Most Wondrous Place!' But you will know when you are there. You will feel it with your heart. Sometimes you will know even before you are there. That is how it was for me the day you brought us home with you. This is A Most Wondrous Place."

My first awareness of chicken wisdom began at that moment. Over the seasons of that first year together, I would learn more about how wise chickens truly are. I would also learn what A Most Wondrous Place means to chickens, and that is why I am writing all of this for you.

But I am getting ahead of myself. First I must tell you about how timid and shy little Gracie became the unlikely leader of my backyard flock. I may ramble a bit, but chickens do that too.

Daffodils in March are for new beginnings. The daffodils in our garden say to us, "I will never forget when our friendship began."

April Daisies

How do you tell baby chicks apart? They are hardly ever still and always eager to explore everything in their new world. But you must be able to tell them apart before you can give them names. Chickens need names to let them know they matter.

Rudy was one of several Rhode Island Reds, but they each had subtle differences in their markings. The Brahmas also had

patches of colored downy feathers to help identify them. The feathers on their feet had patterns too, but they were seldom still long enough to study any of these things. The Emperor and The Empress were the two most regal of them all.

There was only one Plymouth Barred Rock. She was named Mayflower. She never got to say to anyone, "You're like me!"

Telling the Buff Orpingtons apart was not quite so simple. They didn't have any special markings or patches of color. With them, personality helped to tell one from another.

Lefty was easy to spot. He was always curious and always running around to see and do all there was to see and do. He was determined to be the first at everything. Even his comb was the first to develop. That was when I began to suspect he might grow up to be a rooster. His comb began leaning a little to his left, and so he was named Lefty.

Gracie was easy too. She would always hang back from the group or stay close to Bessie. There was also the lump on her side. She kept it facing the wall of the brooder box most of the time. She was afraid the others would spot it and pick on her. As she grew, her fluffy feathers disguised it, and she became less shy.

Bessie looked exactly like the other Buff Orpingtons, but she was easy to find when it was time to rest. She was the one who went to Gracie for companionship. Of the two, Bessie enjoyed playing games with the others more than Gracie did. Even so, she never forgot her friend with the gentle heart.

Bessie often told her stories of the silly things some of the others would do. This was to encourage her to try new things. There were times when Gracie dared to put aside her timidness and join the others in their games. She would tremble with excitement before jumping in and then jumping back out. But you knew she was having fun by the way she would say "Peep!" in the most delightful way.

A baby chick needs to learn how to perch as high as possible. This can keep them safe from predators. I stacked bricks in their brooder box to help them learn.

At first, Gracie was only comfortable on the lowest bricks. Bessie was eager to try any challenge. After reaching each new perching height, she taught Gracie.

Bessie was a very good teacher. She would make sure Gracie was watching her. Then she did the next higher challenge over and over again until Gracie would dare to try. Most of the time, Gracie would do it on the first attempt. Getting her to make that first try often took a good amount of convincing. Bessie kept right on encouraging her. That is what you do when you are best friends forever.

Daisies in April are for innocence and purity. The daisies in our garden say to us, "I want you here with me, and I will help you."

May Wild Roses

If a little chick is ever to quiver with excitement, it will be the first time they stand on a fresh springtime lawn. Then they realize, "This is almost too good to be true. This is the life for me!"

There is warm sunshine to enjoy. There is cool dewy grass to eat. And there are bugs everywhere! In an instant, their entire world is alive with new colors, sounds, and sensations. So could those things make our garden A Most Wondrous Place?

Before then, they had relied on me to bring them treats. Once outside, they could hunt for their own. And they hunted!

Whoever found an earthworm would take it and run. Everyone would follow and hope to grab it away from the lucky chick who had found it.

There was only one direction...forward! And there was only one speed...as fast as their little feet would carry them!

Each worm would get passed around several times. It took great skill to dodge and block and eventually maneuver into a spot where the winner could gobble it down.

It was their game, and they made up their own rules. They owned it, and I simply named it The Worm Olympics Game.

There were times when they were unable to find any worms. They would all line up at the play fence and watch in awe as I dug up a fresh batch of worms from the compost pile. Their eyes grew big, and they peeped and cheeped with delight when I said, "We have some, and they are whoppers!" To them, I was the greatest worm hunter of all time.

Sometimes I acted as referee and supplied the "worm toss" to start a new contest, but the object of the game was always the same. They played simply to have fun with their friends and maybe enjoy an earthworm or two.

Each outdoor adventure gave them new experiences and new knowledge. They would run and play until they were completely exhausted. Then they would flop down on their tummies with their wings spread straight out and take a nap. We called this "going splat." Once they had played their last game for the day, I would gently pick them up and return them to their brooder box for dinner and a warm night of rest. They had all they needed with their friends and a world full of wonders.

"I remember how we used to go splat after playing outside," Gracie told me when we were reminiscing one day. "Bessie and I would always go splat together."

"The two of you were easy to spot. You would be resting your head on Bessie, or she would be resting her head on you. None of the others would go splat like that. Only the two of you."

"Yes, that was truly A Most Wondrous Place."

There were those mysterious words again. Gracie had given me another clue to help me discover for myself what A Most Wondrous Place means to chickens.

"Even now on cold nights, I still see Bessie gently resting her head on your back just like how the two of you used to do."

"And it is still only the two of us who do that," she said. Then she added, "The Promise Of A Most Wondrous Place is that every heart can find a way into it because it is always trying to find a way into every heart."

Wild roses in May are for love and adoration. The wild roses in our garden say to us, "There is always an abundance of the truly good things in life like family and friends to adore."

SUMMER

June Honeysuckles

There was huge excitement when the fourteen chickens moved to their new outdoor home. As they grew, even this new home became more crowded. Soon the ones I was raising for my friends moved out. Then it was just my six with Lefty in charge as the leader.

They had a nice space for running and playing. One entire side of their coop was a wire door. This let in plenty of cool breezes

on the hot summer nights, but it still kept them safe. They could go up their chicken ladder and to the top roosting spot in their coop and feel like they were as tall as me.

If I could go back to any time with my chickens, it would be then. Lefty and The Emperor had not begun crowing, and none of the others were laying eggs. We spent our days simply learning about each other.

Evenings were the best. Once everyone was up in the coop for the night, Gracie and I would usually start a conversation. Then the others joined us or just listened. Sometimes we would all be quiet together and think about what had been said. Chickens can be incredibly contemplative.

When there was barely any light remaining, one of them would begin singing a soothing song to the others. These were beautiful sounds reserved for their closest friends. I always felt honored when they shared these secret melodies with me. They would sing each other to sleep, and I would secure them for the night and then head inside.

When I couldn't get to sleep, I would go back outside and sit with them. Someone, usually Lefty, would ask very softly, "Who's there?"

Chickens are unable to see in the dark. It's their most vulnerable time. Their most fearsome predators are those who are able to see at night like foxes, opossums, and raccoons.

"It's only me," I would say. Those who woke up would greet me and then fall back to sleep. With the stars and the moon in the heavens above me and my chickens beside me, there was nothing more I wanted or needed.

Sometimes they would tell me about a noise they had heard. "It was probably a raccoon," I would say because early some mornings I would see raccoons climbing back up into their ivy covered homes high in the trees. "You don't have anything to worry about," I would reassure them. "I built your home securely, and I won't let anything hurt you."

Gracie got her name one morning when the air was fragrant with honeysuckle. As she moved down the chicken ladder, she pointed her toes and spread out her fluff feathers like the finest frilly dancing gown ever. She was ready for whatever joys and triumphs...or sorrows...the day held for her.

She could hear The Music Of The New Day with her heart. Then she let out that music through the way she glided so gracefully. As I watched her, I could hear the music with my heart too. I did not realize it at the time, but while watching her, I had also stepped into A Most Wondrous Place for a moment.

Honeysuckle blossoms in June are for happiness and a sweet disposition. The honeysuckles in our garden say to us, "Even in darkness, we know we will be brought safely to each new day."

July Nasturtiums

Chickens and gardens naturally go together. They are very good at scratching up weeds and digging in soil. They are even better at eating the bugs that want to eat garden plants, but they are often impatient for those plants to become ripe.

Chickens understand garden food extremely well. Everything is either "food" or "not quite food yet, but almost."

What they don't understand is garden fences. If you were to pass by while they are helping in the garden, their clucking would

sound like, "Why doesn't someone remove this fence for us? Why doesn't someone cut open this watermelon for us?"

Lefty was the most impatient of all. He would pace back and forth without rest, hoping to speed up the ripening process. We all had to be patient with him while he learned to be patient with the watermelons. We saved the first one for the Fourth Of July. One after another, they would take whole bites and then shake the watermelon juice off of their faces. Chickens love watermelon, and they were the last garden treat my six original chickens would share together.

Lefty was learning to crow. His first attempts were weak and embarrassing, but he was persistent. He kept at it until he got it right. My neighbors did not appreciate his desire for perfection.

Soon after our first summer watermelon feast, it was time for Lefty to leave. Moving him out to the country was not easy for any of us. There was only a big friendly dog named Otis for company on the little farm where he went.

As he was settling in to his new home, he looked at me as if to say, "How can you do this to me?" But he did not pace back and forth like before. He had learned to be patient with life, and he gave me time to figure out what I needed to do. The next day, I took Rudy there to be his companion.

A rooster without anyone to protect just doesn't feel like a rooster any more. From his intense watchfulness to his desire to be the first at everything, being a farm rooster was what he had been training for all his life. His patience was rewarded, and he was going to be the best rooster any farm ever had.

Together Lefty and Rudy began raising their own little family. They were soon joined by other farm animals including goats and pigs. Several weeks later, The Emperor began crowing. Then he and The Empress went to a different farm.

Only Gracie and Bessie were left. Our backyard garden felt strangely vacant even with all the flowers and vegetables at the peak of the growing season. Two chickens hardly made a flock at all.

Even though they never said it, I knew both wondered, "Which of us will be next?"

They did not understand city laws, and "no roosters allowed" felt very unfair to them. It meant never seeing friends again.

Each day, I would tell them, "This is your home. You will always be together."

It took time for me to learn to be patient with them as their trust returned. When Blanche and Pearl joined our little flock, we would all learn even more about giving the gift of patience to our friends.

Nasturtiums in July are for victory and conquest. The nasturtiums in our garden say to us, "Persistence and patience will lead to success."

August Sunflowers

From the day I brought Pearl and Blanche home as baby chicks, Pearl was different. She never seemed to understand how to be what the others called "a good normal chicken." They were both White Plymouth Rocks like the big one on top of The Chicken Place Restaurant.

Pearl did the best she could to copy everything Blanche did even though Blanche was just as new to the world as she was. Most importantly, she never gave up hope of one day figuring it

all out. I heard Blanche telling her more than once, "You just have more of what makes a chicken a chicken. That's all."

Pearl was always noisier and more active than any of the others had ever been. She never seemed to be able to completely settle down, not even when it was time to go to sleep. Pearl wanted to entertain and be entertained. Blanche just wanted to eat.

Mishaps seemed to follow Pearl as she grew. She would accidentally turn over the food dish or the water bottle. Instead of going around Blanche, she would step on top of her to get to where she wanted to be. Through it all, Blanche kept loving her.

I had hoped Pearl would get better when she and Blanche were ready to move in with Gracie and Bessie. Instead she only got herself into more trouble. Reasoning from me didn't help. Scolding from the other chickens didn't help. She would look sad, but then she would do something so silly that no one could stay angry at her.

For a time, I wondered if it wouldn't be best to find a nice home out in the country for Blanche and Pearl. Perhaps they would do better where they were the only chickens. It might be a place where Pearl would not need to worry about being an outcast.

Then one day, while I was working in the garden, Pearl ran up to me. Earlier, Bessie had given her another peck on the head to remind her to not cause any trouble. This happened almost every day, and so I thought she was running to let me know she had been pecked again simply for being herself. But she had the happiest expression on her face this time.

"What is it, Pearl?" I asked.

"I just found A Most Wondrous Place!" she said, pointing toward where Blanche was sitting under the sunflowers.

After making a joyful little hop up into the air and stretching out her wings as if to give me a hug, she ran back to where Blanche was sitting. She plopped herself down and chattered happily.

As Pearl leaned against Blanche, they looked up to the tops of the sunflowers together. A goldfinch landed on one of the faded flower heads and took a few seeds for himself and dropped a few for them. "Blanche, this is A Most Wondrous Place," she said. "It truly is."

After that, I never thought about finding a new home for Blanche and Pearl. Somehow it would all work out.

Pearl loves our annual summertime patch of sunflowers almost as much as I do. But they were not what she meant when she said, "I just found A Most Wondrous Place!"

August sunflowers are for longevity and loyalty. The sunflowers in our garden say to us, "Our truest friends are those who are by our side no matter what."

AUTUMN

September Morning Glories

Chickens need a schedule almost as much as they need other chickens. They do not easily adjust to anyone else's schedule. If you have backyard chickens, you must adjust to their schedule. You must also have a nice breakfast ready when their day begins.

So I wake up in the morning even before they do to make their breakfast salad. It's a lot of chopping and there has to be variety since not everyone likes everything.

I do this partly because it is no fun facing six grumpy hens when there is no breakfast salad laid out for them. Mostly I do it because I love them. That is also why I let them use my jeans

and shoes to wipe off their beaks after they have finished eating. My chickens need me, even if it is just to be their napkin.

Bessie had begun laying eggs when my chickens had their first taste of pumpkin. It was time to celebrate and everyone was excited. Pumpkins are bigger than watermelons, and so pumpkins must be better than watermelons. That was what they thought.

I cut into the pumpkin and scooped out a handful of seeds. They looked at the seeds. They looked at me. They looked back at the seeds. The expression on their faces told me, "These seeds are too big, and we are hungry!"

So I learned to roast pumpkin seeds to make them smaller and crunchier. They quickly became a favorite for all my chickens.

After learning this important lesson, I believed I had mastered pumpkins. All I needed to do was cut up the remaining pumpkin, and they would feast happily!

But I was wrong again. It sat for days. No one touched it. There was not even an inquisitive peck. And so I learned to steam pumpkin to make it softer and easier to eat. They liked it, but not as much as the roasted seeds.

At last, we were all very happy, but I did wonder if my chickens weren't acting a little like beautiful, but spoiled, princesses. The truth is they do not think of themselves like that at all. They do not realize their own beauty. Maybe that is the way it is with all truly beautiful things.

My neighborhood is home for many kinds of songbirds, but my chickens never compare themselves to the songbirds. They never feel badly because they can't sing like them. Chickens have their own special kind of singing. But they will still listen to and appreciate those other songs without trying to copy them.

My house is across the street from a vacant lot and a marshy branch of the river. Tall and graceful white egrets will wade there, but my chickens never compare themselves to the egrets. My chickens watch with interest, but they never try to walk or stand gracefully like them. I do imagine they might like to go fishing or frogging with them. It would be fun even if their much shorter beaks and legs would make them look silly flopping around in the water.

My chickens don't worry about not being the best singers. They don't worry about not having the longest legs. They don't worry about looking beautiful. Yet when they stand in amazement of the beauty surrounding them in our backyard garden, they become even more beautiful to me.

Morning glories in September remind us of affection and mortality. The morning glories in our garden say to us, "There are more kinds of beauty than we can ever count. The greatest kind of beauty will never fade away even when the day is done."

October Goldenrods

Autumn is a wonderful time to get outside and do some work in the yard. Temperatures are cooler, and there are always plenty of chores that need doing.

It is also a season to consider bounty and prosperity as we do the last harvesting of the garden. The first frost will come soon. There will be no more fresh vegetables from the garden until sweet peas in the early spring.

Autumn always makes me wonder if I have accomplished anything in life that is real and lasting. With the season's bounty also comes the season's decay. If it hasn't been done yet it probably will not be done. There are only so many springs left.

My new temporary job started early in the morning. It was so early that my chickens couldn't find their way down the chicken ladder without my help with a flashlight. They did not like this change. The days were getting shorter, and sunset was coming sooner. The new season was stealing greater bites of our precious evening time together. Soon it would be completely dark when I returned home as well.

With the shorter days, a certain cold sadness settled on us. Autumn is the season to end all we have tried to start but failed to finish. It lets us begin the forgetting and the forgiving. Often we have to forget our failures and forgive ourselves for failing. Sometimes we must forgive ourselves for not having enough hope, not having enough faith, or just not having.

Winter will soon bring a chance for new hopes and new dreams. My chickens will cover their heads with a wing, and I will cover mine with a quilt. We will close our eyes and shut out the cold. Then at last, we will dream of the world and the life we want for ourselves and those we love. We will hope our distant friends are as safe and as warm and as loved as we are. Our hearts will be warmed by our memories of time spent with them.

Spring will come again to our garden home. It will bring a new chance to do again what we had tried and failed to do before. And it will also bring more earthworms to hunt!

But first we must wait for autumn and winter to have their turns at touching our lives. On that lovely October day, those were only passing thoughts. I took a break from chores and sat with Blanche and Pearl. "Show me how pretty you are," I said.

They moved from the dappled shade to a spot where their white feathers reflected the sunlight most magnificently. In that one moment, I felt so rich and prosperous I couldn't imagine wanting anything more.

Then Pearl nudged herself between the fencing and Blanche who was already as close as she could get to soak up the sun's warmth. But Pearl was persistent, as only Pearl can be, and Blanche relented. She surrendered her prime spot and shifted over to one with less sunlight.

Pearl was happy once more. For her, it was not about having the sunniest spot. In no time at all, she was up and off and looking for something else to do. She had simply needed to feel confident in the great wealth of love and friendship she had with Blanche.

Goldenrods in October are for good fortune. The goldenrods in our garden say to us, "Our friends and family make us wealthy beyond measure."

November Chrysanthemums

Boundaries and fences are sometimes annoying, but they can protect us from some bad things we don't want. Even so, they can also keep us from some good things too. One of those good things is knowing what life is like for someone else.

With my new job, I was away for the first time for most of the day. Bessie finally felt like a leader with three other chickens to keep watch over while I was at work. At last, she had a chance to show her best leadership skills.

She stood so proudly when I told her, "Bessie, you're in charge until I get back."

She took her new duties very seriously. She protected Gracie as she had always done, but now there were also two younger

chickens, Blanche and Pearl. She would need to keep them in line and guide them through those awkward teenage weeks.

She patrolled for danger, just as Lefty had done, back and forth along the fencing. There were even some times when she tried to crow like Lefty, even though no sound came out.

At first, everyone was glad to see me when I got home. Bessie looked relieved because she could relax and let me worry about keeping everyone safe. As time went by, they became accustomed to our new routine, and everyone would be resting contently when I got home. Only Pearl would still hop up to welcome me back again. That's just how she has always been and probably always will be.

But one day when I got home, no one was sitting. Everyone was pacing frantically. Even Pearl did not hop around and give me her usual happy greeting. Something had happened while I was away. When I looked closer at Bessie, I could see two scabbed-over gash marks on the top of her head, one on each side of her comb.

I asked Bessie to tell me what had happened, and she did. The others listened and nodded in agreement. She even went up into their coop to show me more. She talked and pointed with her beak and talked some more and pointed to a different spot.

When she pointed to the blood splatters on the inside walls of their coop, I knew how deep her trauma must have been. She went on and on for the longest time. All I could say was, "I know, Honey, I know."

But I didn't know, not the way I wanted to know. I understood every word she was saying as she acted out the details of exactly what had happened, but I was not a chicken.

I did not know in the same way Bessie and the others did. There were no English words to explain it, only Chicken words. Even those seemed insufficient to me.

We cried together that day.

There was an unseen boundary which I was unable to cross. More than anything, I wanted to let Bessie know how I shared her feelings even though I had not shared her experience.

Somehow knowing a friend also shares your feelings makes difficult times less difficult. Gracie and the others knew, and they consoled her while I listened and nodded in agreement. Finally she settled down.

A stray cat had found a weak place in the fencing between the coop and the run. It had managed to get a paw through. Then it had tried to make the gap big enough to get its whole body through. Cat claws are much sharper than any chicken's beak. For Bessie, it had been terrifying and a kind of terror only a chicken can know when protecting friends.

Since then, the cats have started taking different paths through our yard, usually in the shadows under the shrubs and brambles. The chickens will sound alarm whenever one is in sight. Everyone, even Pearl who would rather play, is watchful.

What happened that day changed Bessie. She continued to be the leader for a while, but began holding back more and more until Gracie was ready to take over as the new leader. Even after her scars healed, she was not the same. On the outside, the back half of her comb flopped down limply to one side, but it was more than just that. On the inside, she seemed nervous and unsure of herself even after I repaired the gap the cat had made in the fencing.

What happened that day changed me as well. Hearing Bessie recount the story the way she did convinced me never to think of any chickens as "just chickens." They care very much about each other.

Bessie had defended Gracie who she had known and loved since the day they hatched together. She defended Blanche who she hardly knew. And she had also defended Pearl who she mostly just put up with on a good day and would chase around angrily on a bad day.

Although she could have, Bessie never told me, "You don't know what it's like. You're not a chicken." She knew I would have traded places with her that day if I could have. But there was a boundary I could not cross. I could never be a chicken. I could never trade places with Bessie or any of them.

Without a doubt, trading places is what Bessie did that day. Even if it would have meant her death to save Gracie or Blanche or Pearl, she would have done it.

I stayed with them late into the night and thought back to when I first brought Gracie and Bessie home. I thought about how Gracie had told me she didn't know what happened to the other chicks at The Feed And Seed Store. I thought about how she was determined to stay with Bessie if she could. I thought about how she had hoped whatever happened to them would be something better and not something worse. I wondered if this little garden in the city was really something better for them.

Just before they drifted off to sleep, I heard Bessie tell Gracie, "Even with all that happened today and the bad things that can hurt us, I still believe this is A Most Wondrous Place."

The next day, Bessie began to teach Gracie all she needed to know to be a leader. It was just like how she had taught her to reach higher and higher perching spots when they were just little chicks.

My timid little Gracie who had started life with so much against her was to become the new leader.

Chrysanthemums in November are for rest and recovery after a long challenge. They are also for lasting friendship, loyalty, and devotion. The chrysanthemums in our garden say to us, "This is what it means to be a leader and a friend."

WINTER

December Hollies

There is pure delight in the moment a baby chick first stands on your foot. It is an indescribable joy. You barely feel any weight at all, only perhaps the light landing when they hop up onto your shoe. It is a moment you never want to end because it is filled with such innocence and trust. You may think, "This is how life is intended to be," and you would be right.

Even when grown, my chickens will still stand on my feet from time to time, and they are still amazingly light. They perform

beautiful arabesques and breathtaking leaps from a foot, from a lap, from a perch. Every movement brings such joy.

It took some time before Gracie shared her most secret desire of becoming a real ballerina. Sometimes it takes a leap of faith to say our dreams aloud, but it is easier to share dreams with a friend.

All my girls enjoy the art of dance, but Gracie sees it as her gift and what she loves the most. I do not have the heart to tell her, or any of them really, that it's simply not possible. Chickens can't be ballet dancers on a real ballet stage with an orchestra.

So they dance. I take my old record player out into the backyard and put on their favorite classical albums from the thrift store. And they dance. One day we will create our own backyard ballet and call it The Rose Garden Princess.

But events beyond our control had moved Gracie to the top position of our little backyard flock. She had to put aside her ballet dreams for a time to assume Bessie's role as protector. That is just what friends do without complaining.

After several weeks of being the leader, Gracie seemed worried and trying to hide it. So I scattered around some sunflower kernels. While everyone else was enjoying their treat, I called Gracie to me to see what was bothering her.

"There's been a monster creeping around here when it starts to get dark and before you come home," she said all at once.

She felt better just by saying something about it. So I asked her to tell me what it looked like, and she did. She even tried to move like it did when it was sneaking up on them.

"That sounds like a sewer rat," I said. "Did it have a long, almost-naked pink tail that looks like it has been chewed?"

"Yes," she said, relieved I knew what she was talking about. It hurt me to see her trying to appear brave while carrying such a heavy responsibility all alone.

"I have seen it creeping along next to the curb by the storm drain. He looks old and mangy, but the two good teeth he has left could still be dangerous.

"Gracie, Sweetie, you were right to be alarmed. Remember though, it's an old sewer rat, not a monster. He might like for you to think he's a monster so you will be afraid of him, but he is not. He will only become a monster if you let him become one in your mind. Do you understand?"

She nodded.

"But tell me, why didn't you say something before now? Is it because you didn't want to make the others scared?"

She nodded again and then added in her softest voice, "I didn't want you to think I wasn't a good leader. I don't know how to protect anyone, not even myself, from something so mean."

She waited to see if I was disappointed in her. When she saw I wasn't, she continued.

"He says the most evil things to us. He makes fun of us and tells us everything that is wrong with us. I just stand there, looking him in the eyes and not moving." Then her voice trailed off as she added, "But I don't say anything. I don't do anything."

She lowered her head, waiting for me to say something, even if it was something she didn't want to hear.

"You are a better leader than you realize, Gracie."

"But I never wanted to be a leader. I only ever wanted to be a friend."

"I know. That's what makes you a good leader. Just don't let your fears get the best of you. Are you afraid right now?"

"No. But that is because you are here." She looked up and saw I wasn't angry with her at all.

"And when I'm not here, have I made things safe for you even when I'm not here? You are more important to me than anything. I would never leave you without making sure you are protected from that nasty old rat. You do believe that, don't you?"

Gracie took time to think this over. She looked at the strong fencing I had used to build their home. She looked at how everything they needed was safe and secure, just like they were. She nodded. Nothing could ever get inside again.

"And what do I tell you every morning before I leave for work?"

"You say to be good to each other and take care of each other. Then you say to never forget how much you love us."

I smiled my biggest smile and said, "Exactly right. You are mine and I am yours, and I love you more than anything in this garden. Are you afraid when you think about how much I love you?"

"No!" she said with so much amazement she actually surprised herself. "No! I'm not afraid then!" She fluffed out all of her feathers like she was a new baby chick ready for a fresh start.

"Gracie, let's turn that old sewer rat into part of our ballet about The Rose Garden Princess. We need an evil character to make the story more interesting. We can call him The Evil King Of Darkest Night. What do you say? Can you only pretend to be afraid? For the ballet?"

"Yes!" she clucked again and again, overflowing with more joy than I had seen in the longest time.

Gracie hurried back to the others to get a few sunflower kernels before they were all gone. She even did a few ballet leaps along the way. At least they certainly looked like ballet leaps in my eyes even if no one else's.

She is so beautiful, my beloved little Gracie, and one day we will dance together, just as our hearts already do. It will just take another leap of faith.

Holly in December is for domestic happiness, defense, and foresight. The hollies in our garden say to us, "The only power that fear and evil truly have is when we forget how much our friends and family love us."

January Snowdrops

"Will you take Amelia?" was a question that would change my life with my backyard chickens more than I could have ever imagined. "She needs you."

My friends were in a very rural part of their city, but they still needed five and a half acres of land to have any chickens. Amelia and the others in her flock of twelve needed new homes.

I had watched them growing up, and Amelia was definitely special. She did everything before anyone else even thought of

doing it. She loved flying to high perching places no one else could reach. So it was hard to understand why my friends had said, "She needs you." She seemed so independent to me.

Amelia is a Plymouth Barred Rock, but she has always insisted on being treated as a person, not as a chicken. She was surely destined for greatness, but greatness doesn't happen very often for chickens. It seemed impossible as she moved to our garden.

Emily, with her gentle and easy-going nature, came along for companionship. She is a dainty little lady who always minds her manners and expects others to do the same. As a Golden Laced Wyandotte, her brown markings and iridescent feathers make her stand out. She also adores Amelia with all of her heart.

For weeks, I planned and built a new home for six chickens. It would have plenty of wing-flapping room for them and lots of walking-around room for me. At every chance, I would tell them, "You have no idea how wonderful your new home will be!"

I had made a temporary home for Amelia and Emily across the garden path from the one for Gracie, Bessie, Blanche, and Pearl. This was to get them accustomed to each other until they could all be one new flock in their new home.

Each evening, I would cut up grapes and apples and sit between the two groups and take turns hand feeding them. This was to let them know they were the same. It is not always easy to introduce new chickens to an existing flock.

They often spoke to each other across the garden path. At first, they had distinctive dialects of "City Chicken" and "Country Chicken." These soon blended together as one, just the way I hoped they would blend together as one flock.

It was not easy building during the coldest part of that winter. I had to wait for the occasional warmer days when the ground was not as frozen to dig a deep foundation. Predators can also dig, and they will dig under fencing to get to chickens.

Slowly it came together. Everyone enjoyed my nightly progress reports except for Amelia. She would listen, but never expressed any excitement like the others. And she paced almost constantly. She did not like her temporary confined space. She missed her big backyard in the country where she could fly freely with her hatch-mates. She seemed miserable.

Emily adapted to the change much better than Amelia. She enjoyed looking out at the garden. She asked dozens of questions about everything and always very politely too. Even when Emily encouraged her, Amelia would not speak to me. It seemed as if she would never accept her new home. Whatever A Most Wondrous Place was for chickens, I was certain Amelia would never find it in my backyard garden or with me.

Snowdrops in January are for sympathy, hope, and rebirth. The snowdrops in our garden say to us, "Every new friendship is a chance for a new life of possibilities."

February Crocuses

For the longest time, wrens were my main backyard birds. It was always enjoyable to sit in my sunroom and watch them looking for food and doing all the things wrens do. And wrens have a lot to do! They seldom sit quietly like chickens.

My chickens take up much more space in our backyard garden than the little wrens, but they all get along quite well. They see each other as equally important to life. With a little hunting and pecking, there is an abundance of all good things for everyone.

The wrens were the original owners of my backyard, but they enjoy sharing it with chickens. That is because chickens love to scratch around. When they get carried away, they spread seeds in all directions. A good amount usually ends up outside the run for the wrens to pick up and eat.

In the winter, my chickens and I watch the wrens. They don't seem bothered by my presence now because of the chickens. We enjoy their quick hopping and darting movements from place to place. The backyard would not feel the same without their joyfulness. Sometimes thrushes and chickadees join them.

There have been times when wrens have visited inside the chickens' run and coop. Perhaps it was to evade a larger predator or get a little closer to the chickens' supply of grain and seeds. There have also been times when I have opened the chicken coop in the morning, and a little wren has flown out.

My chickens never really care why those wrens had come to share their home for the night. What matters is they were there in need of friendship, and they were birds too. My chickens seem to understand how they, along with the wrens, are both together my beloved birds. They know friendship can connect one life to another.

Amelia seemed to understand this more than any of the others. There were always more wrens watching her and talking with her. Perhaps they shared their stories of life outside our garden home. But listening to tales of daring flights could never take the place of soaring freely. I was sure of it.

When the time came to move into their new backyard home, Emily was first. She seemed to panic a little because she was separated from Amelia for the first time. Soon her curiosity took over, and she began exploring. She hopped up on a new straw bale to get a better look at everything. In the new home, she could see more of the garden. As she examined the buds on the branches, she was able to imagine how they would all look when spring finally came to our garden.

Amelia moved in next. When I picked her up she felt much lighter than I had expected. Later I realized she likes to fluff out her feathers. This gives extra warmth and also makes her look bigger and braver than she really might be.

I thought back to the words, "She needs you." It didn't seem like she needed me at all.

When I gently placed her down, she did not look around to see her new home like Emily had done. She looked way up to my face and into my eyes. Then she hopped straight up no more than six inches off of the ground. That was all her little body would allow without any wing-flapping for lift.

Amelia simply wanted to be picked up and hugged. As I lifted her up, there was no hesitation in her body or in her heart. I held her close to my chest and kissed the top of her head.

Then Amelia spoke to me at last. "That is all I ever wanted," she said. "Some things are more important than flying. This is A Most Wondrous Place."

Then I understood what A Most Wondrous Place means to chickens. I felt it in my heart too. I needed Amelia as much as she needed me.

"I love you, Amelia. This is your home for as long as you want it to be. I will never give you away. I will never keep you from leaving. This truly is A Most Wondrous Place because we are here together with Love."

Crocuses in February are for cheerfulness and gladness. The crocuses in our garden say to us, "Every life can be transformed by Love."

Epilogue (Another Conversation With Gracie)

"So how is the book about A Most Wondrous Place coming along?" asked Gracie.

"It's finished except for the very last part. I want to say something more about the friendship you and Bessie have always shared, but the words are not so easy."

"What do you mean?"

"Chickens like you seem to be so much better at friendship than me. I have good intentions, but there are times when I think I could be a better friend. I don't want to let anyone down."

"You've never let me down," she said.

"What do you mean?"

"You always wish me a good morning, and you always wish me a good night."

"There has to be more to it than that."

"You watch over me and the others. I remember how you would sit out with us at night when we hadn't learned how to go up the ladder into our coop."

Gracie looked directly at my eyes to make sure I was paying attention. "You even did that after we learned to go up the ladder to get to the coop on our own. You didn't have to do that, but you did it anyway. You have always been my friend. I knew you

58

would be from the moment you whispered into the shoe box at The Feed And Seed Store."

"And what did I whisper?"

"After the sales clerk said there was something wrong with me, you whispered into the shoebox that I was so much more than good enough. You let me know that I mattered."

"You are quite remarkable, Gracie."

"What do you mean?" she asked. She was still unaware of just how beautiful she is in my eyes simply by being herself.

"When you were a little chick, you seemed so lost and alone, especially when you were trying to shelter yourself. It wasn't easy for you.

"I never imagined you would become the leader you are today. You have overcome so much. You even put aside your dreams of being a ballerina to watch over your friends. Now you shelter Bessie and all the others."

"You have always sheltered me."

"Do you really think so?" I asked. "Bessie was there by your side and right with you from the beginning."

"Yes, but yours was the hand that fed and protected both of us before we recognized your voice. Yours was the hand that loved both of us before we recognized your face. We all need someone to be our friend and to shelter us. You are a part of what makes this A Most Wondrous Place."

"And so are you, Gracie. I have a special surprise for you."

"You know I love surprises. What is it?"

"I did write some about how you love to dance ballet. Even though we are going to make a special book together about The Rose Garden Princess, dancing is in this book too."

"You did that just for me, didn't you?"

"You know I did. But there is an even bigger surprise. In one very special drawing, I hid a pair of your ballet slippers."

"Really?"

"They are hidden away so people have to look for them. It's just like they have to look for what chickens mean when they call somewhere A Most Wondrous Place. The ballet slippers are hidden away as a reminder of my promises to you because you are my friend. You are so much more than good enough."

Gracie immediately wanted to look through the drawings for the hidden ballet slippers.

"Will you give me a hint where to look for them?"

"You know it will be more fun finding them on your own. It's that way with so many things in life, especially things like finding A Most Wondrous Place."

"So what is the name of the book?" she asked.

"Why don't you tell me what it should be?"

"A Most Wondrous Place. That would be a nice name. Will you tell about how we love and take care of one another?"

"Yes, absolutely."

"That's good. Those are the most important things we do. Chickens don't have anything to give each other except ourselves."

"I know, Gracie. That is why you chickens know so much about A Most Wondrous Place."

We spent the rest of the evening together before the sun went down. Gracie sat in my lap. I would read, and Gracie would look at the drawings to find her ballet slippers. She found them, just as I knew she would. They were exactly where The Rose Garden Princess would have left them.

About The Author

John Spiers is a writer, artist, and guardian to a small flock of chickens who live in the center of his backyard garden.

While he often produced small writing and drawing projects over the years, he never found his creative purpose until he decided to raise some baby chicks. They became the characters in his stories and the subjects of his drawings.

His work seeks to share the same joy he feels when spending time with his chickens along with bits of "chicken wisdom" about life which he has learned from them.

About This Book

Along with sharing what he has learned from his chickens, the author also enjoys hiding things in his illustrations. His chickens enjoy finding them, and perhaps you will as well. If you are curious and persistent, you can find a pair of Gracie's ballet slippers that he promised to put in every book.

It may help your search if you imagine sitting with the author and his chickens in their backyard garden home. It truly is A Most Wondrous Place with many more secrets and promises to share.

GraciePress.com

CPSIA information can be obtained
at www.ICGtesting.com
Printed in the USA
LVHW071129070123
736413LV00009B/361

9 781736 633809